Fun Ways to Learn the Whole Story of Jesus and His Love

Jesus Is Alive!

Creative Bible-Learning
Activities for Children
Ages 6-12

Copyright © 1991 by Tracy Leffingwell Harrast. All rights reserved.
Published by David C. Cook Church Ministry Resources, a division of Cook Communications Ministries International.
Printed in the United States of America.

All puzzles and Bible activities are based on the NIV.

Scripture taken from the Holy Bible, New International Version, Copyright © 1973,
1978, 1984 International Bible Society.
Used by permission of Zondervan Bible Publishers.

Book Design by Tabb Associates
Cover Illustration by Gary Locke
Interior Illustrations by Anne Kennedy

10 9 8 7 6 5

THIS BOOK BELONGS TO:

_____

To My Children and Others Who Read This Book

Can you imagine how happy Jesus' followers were when they saw Him alive after He had died? We'll be happy when we see Him, too! We can get ready for His return by trusting Him as our Savior and following Him as our Lord. It will be a great day when Jesus comes back and takes us to live with Him in heaven!

—Tracy L. Harrast

Jesus Is Alive!
CONTENTS

The First Easter, Part 1

Early on Sunday morning, Mary Magdalene, Mary the mother of James, Salome, and other women went 2 visit the 🪦 where 🧔 had been buried 2 put more spices on His body. The 👭 were wondering how they would get the heavy 🪨 away from the opening of the 🪦. When they looked ⬆ , they 🪚 that the 🪨 had already been rolled away. When they looked inside the 🪦 , they 🪚 that the body of 🧔 was gone!

There had been an 🌍 +quake. An 👼 had come and rolled the 🪨 away from the 🪦 . The 👼 was bright like ⚡ . His 👕 were white as ❄ . The 💂 were so afraid of the 👼 that they shook and then fainted.

👼 were sitting where the body of 🧔 had been. The 👭 bowed their faces. An 👼 told them 🚫 2 🐝 afraid. He knew they were looking 4 🧔 , who was crucified. The 👼 told them, "He is 🚫 here; He has risen! 🚦 , tell His disciples and Peter."

☐ *Draw a star in this box when you've read Matthew 28:1-8; Mark 16:1-8; Luke 24:1-8; and John 20:1, 2.*

The First Easter, Part 2

Put these words where they belong in the story: FATHER, ANGELS, LORD, PETER, JESUS, GARDENER, BODY, CRYING.

Mary Magdalene told Peter and John, "They have taken the 1._____ out of the tomb, and we don't know where they have put Him!" 2._____ and John went to see for themselves. They saw the linens that had been wrapped around Jesus, but His 3._____ was gone. Peter and John went home, but Mary stayed at the tomb. She was crying and when she stooped down to look into the tomb, she saw two 4._____ sitting where Jesus' body had been. They asked, "Why are you 5._____?" She answered, "They have taken my Lord away, and I don't know where they have put Him."

Then Mary turned around and saw 6._____ standing there. At first Mary thought He was the 7._____. Jesus asked her, "Why are you crying? Who is it you are looking for?" She said, "If you have carried Him away, tell me where you have put Him, and I will get Him." Then Jesus said, "Mary." As soon as He said that, Mary recognized that it was Jesus! She said, "Teacher!" Jesus said, "Do not hold on to me, for I have not yet returned to the 8._____. Go instead to my brothers and tell them, 'I am returning to my Father and your Father, to my God and your God.'"

Mary Magdalene told the disciples she had seen Jesus and gave them His message.

Draw a star in this box when you've read Matthew 28:9, 10; Mark 16:9-11; Luke 24:9-12; and John 20:2-18.

Make Glove Puppets

You can make these fun puppets and use them to act out the Easter story.

What You Need

- two thin latex gloves (from a pharmacy) or old rubber gloves
- scissors
- permanent markers
- cup that isn't clear
- paper circle

What You Do

1. Cut the fingers and thumbs off of the gloves.

2. Draw Mary Magdalene and four women on the fingers and thumb from one glove. Now draw Jesus on the other glove's thumb, the angels on the index and middle finger, Peter on the ring finger, and John on the pinkie.

3. Read parts 1 and 2 of "The First Easter" (pages 5 and 6) again.

4. Rehearse your show. Put all of the puppets except Jesus on your fingers. Put the Jesus puppet inside the cup "tomb" with the paper circle "stone" in front of it. Show what happened during the earthquake. Tell the rest of the story with the puppets at the cup "tomb."

5. When your show is ready, you can perform it for your family and friends on Easter Sunday.

Make an Egg Scene

What You Need

- clean, dry eggshell
- bowl
- manicure scissors
- modeling clay
- angels from this page
- jar lid
- silver glitter
- Easter grass
- sewing trim (braid, lace, or ribbon)
- glue

What You Do

1. Color and cut out the angels from this page. Mold a small ball of clay around the tab of the angels. Stick the clay to the middle of the lid so the angels are upright.

2. Carefully trim the bottom of the eggshell so it is fairly even. Carefully cut an opening that will be the entrance of the tomb. If the eggshell cracks, don't get discouraged; just try again with another eggshell.

3. Gently rub glue inside the tomb, sprinkle glitter in it, shake it around, and pour the excess glitter onto a paper towel.

4. Glue the eggshell tomb to the lid with the angels inside.

5. Rub a small amount of glue on the floor of the tomb and covering the clay. Sprinkle silver glitter; shake it gently; pour the excess onto a paper towel.

6. Spread glue on the lid around the outside of the tomb. Press Easter grass on it.

7. Cut a piece of sewing trim to fit around the lid. Attach it with glue.

Easter Story Hunt

What You Need

- paper and pen
- scissors
- plastic eggs

What You Do

1. Reread parts one and two of "The First Easter" (pages 5 and 6) and write the Easter story in your own words.

2. Number the paragraphs in their correct order, then cut them out and roll them into coils. Stick each paragraph inside an egg.

3. Ask a grown-up to hide the eggs.

4. Hunt for the eggs with your classmates, friends, or family.

5. When you have found all of the eggs, sit in a circle. Open the eggs to find out who has which numbered paragraph. Then have each person read the paragraph from the egg he or she found.

Christian Meanings of Easter Symbols

Many of the symbols that we see at Easter have been around for nearly two thousand years! Over the years the meanings of some of these symbols have been forgotten. If we know the meanings, these symbols can remind us of Jesus and the reason we're happy at Easter. *Read what each symbol means, and then color the pictures.*

Cross

The cross reminds us that Jesus died for us so that believers will live with Him in heaven forever.

Easter Eggs and Chicks

Eggs look a little like tombs, and something alive comes out of them. They remind us that Jesus was in a tomb for three days, but He came out alive!

Easter Lilies

These pure white flowers spring to life from bulbs that looked like tombs all winter. They remind us that believers will have a pure new life after they die because Jesus came back to life after He was crucified.

Lambs

In Old Testament times, death "passed over" the homes of families that had lamb's blood on the doorpost. Passover lambs were like Jesus. Their blood kept the Israelites alive. If we have faith that our sins are forgiven because Jesus' blood was shed for us, we will live forever with God.

Jonah in the Great Fish

This symbol isn't common at Easter anymore. Jesus compared Himself to Jonah and said that like Jonah was in the great fish for three days, Jesus would be in the earth for three days.

New Clothes

People who were baptized the week before Easter wore new clothes as a symbol of their new life in Jesus. Other people also began to wear new clothes at Easter as a symbol that they would have a new life after they died because Jesus died and was resurrected.

Make Easter Stickers

It's easy to make your own stickers for Easter cards and envelopes. *First draw small pictures of Christian Easter symbols and cut them out. Then follow these directions to turn your drawings into stickers.*

What You Need

- 2 tablespoons flavored gelatin
- 2 tablespoons boiling water (if you're completing this activity in a classroom, use very hot water from a Thermos)
- cup
- spoon
- wax paper

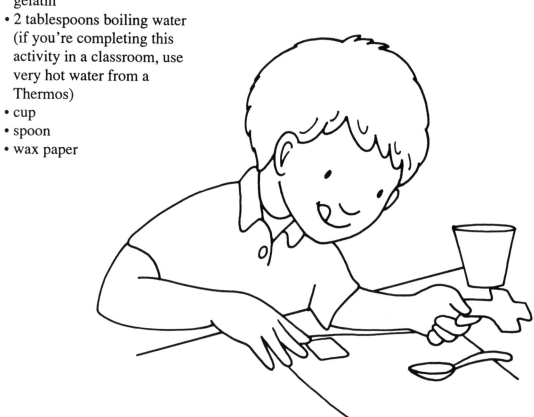

What You Do

1. Measure the gelatin and pour it into the cup. Measure the water and pour it into the cup. Stir until the gelatin dissolves.
2. Lay your cutout drawings of Easter symbols facedown on the wax paper.
3. Use the spoon to spread a little of the mixture on the back of each cutout drawing.
4. When stickers are dry, you can lick them and stick them on homemade Easter cards and envelopes. If you make your own cards, you may want to write inside each card the Christian meaning of the Easter symbol you put on the card and envelope.

Easter Eggs

Eggs are one of the most common symbols of Easter. An egg looks a little like a tomb, and something alive comes out of it. It reminds us that Jesus was in a tomb for three days, but He came out alive!

A Great Christian Custom

When Greek children see each other on Easter, they each hold out a colored egg and tap them together gently. One person says, "Christ is risen," and the other answers, "Truly, He is risen." Tell your friends about this custom and see if you can get it going where you live.

Fun Ways to Decorate Eggs

(Use symbols that remind you of Jesus.)

• Before you color your eggs, draw on some of them with crayons or paint on them with rubber cement. If you use rubber cement, you can peel off the design after you've colored the eggs.

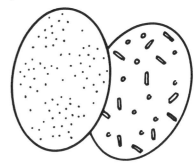

After you've colored the eggs:

• Glue on designs cut from felt.

• Glue on glitter or cake decorating sprinkles.

• Attach small stickers.

• Be creative and come up with some unique ideas and designs of your own!

Easter Chicks

Chicks are a symbol of Easter because they come out of eggs alive, and Jesus came out of the tomb alive.

Make a Cotton Ball Chick

What You Need

- cotton ball
- small rubber band (the kind for dental braces are great)
- orange felt or paper triangle
- glue
- marker
- half of an eggshell, rinsed and dried

What You Do

1. Wrap a small rubber band around the cotton ball to separate it into a head and body.
2. Glue on an orange felt or paper triangle for a beak.
3. Draw eyes with a marker.
4. Glue the cotton ball chick into the bottom of the eggshell.

Make a Boiled Egg Hatching Chick

What You Need

- boiled egg
- plastic knife
- toothpick
- food coloring

What You Do

1. Peel the boiled egg and rinse it.
2. Use a plastic knife to cut a jagged line around the white, being careful not to cut into the yolk.
3. Carefully pull off the top white part.
4. Draw a beak and eyes on the yolk using a toothpick dipped in food coloring.

Eggshell Mosaic Cross

The cross reminds us that Jesus died for us so that believers will live with Him in heaven forever.

What You Need

- 3 eggshells of different colors (saved from Easter eggs and dried)
- cardboard
- pencil
- ruler
- scissors
- 3 cups
- glue
- paper clip
- strong tape

What You Do

1. Use a pencil and ruler to make the outline of a cross on a piece of cardboard. Cut it out, then draw two other crosses inside the first cross.

2. Divide the eggshells into the cups by color. Crumble the shells into small pieces.

3. Spread glue evenly on the center cross. Sprinkle one color of eggshell pieces onto the glue. Gently shake off the extra pieces and let it dry a bit.

4. Spread glue evenly on the second cross. Sprinkle a different color of eggshell pieces on it, and gently shake off the extras. Let this layer dry a little and repeat with a different color around the last cross. Let it all dry completely.

5. Tape a paper clip to the back of the cross so you can hang your new mosaic.

Jonah and the Great Fish

Jonah and the great fish were once common Easter symbols. Jesus even compared His death to Jonah's time inside the fish. Jesus said that like Jonah was in the fish for three days, He would be in the earth for three days.

Make Jonah-in-the-Great Fish Soap

What You Need for Jonah

- 3/4 cup Ivory Snow soap powder
- 1 tablespoon warm water
- 1 drop red food coloring

What You Need for the Great Fish

- 1 1/2 cups Ivory Snow soap powder
- 2 tablespoon warm water
- 3 drops blue food coloring
- toothpick

What You Do

1. To make soap clay for Jonah, mix the soap powder, food coloring, and water into a clay. Mold a small, simple man's head.
2. Mix the ingredients for the Great Fish to make a clay.
3. Shape a hollow fish out of the clay, and put Jonah inside. Be sure Jonah shows in the fish's open mouth.
4. Use a little of the blue clay to make eyes to press into Jonah's face. Use a little of the pink clay to make eyes to press onto the blue whale.

Draw a star in this box when you've read Matthew 12:39-41; 16:4; and Luke 11:29-32.

Make a Lamb Cupcake

In Old Testament times, death "passed over" the homes of families that had the blood of a lamb on the doorpost. Jews remembered this event by celebrating a holiday called Passover. During this holiday they killed a Passover Lamb. Jesus was killed at this time of year, and He is like our Passover Lamb. Putting lamb's blood on doorposts kept Israelites alive, and we have everlasting life if we believe our sins are forgiven because Jesus' blood was shed for us.

What You Need

- chocolate cupcake and white frosting
- 2 flat chocolate cookies
- 3 black jelly beans
- 2 short pieces of red string licorice

What You Do

1. Remove the wrapper from the cupcake. Turn the cupcake upside down, and cover only the sides with a thick layer of frosting. Spread the frosting so it looks fluffy.
2. Stick cookies onto the frosted sides for ears.
3. Use frosting to stick the jelly beans to the top for eyes and a nose. Also use frosting to stick on the licorice strings for a mouth.
4. Make cupcake lambs for your family and friends. As you give away each cupcake, you can tell why lambs are a symbol of Easter.

Make Paper Easter Lilies

These pure white flowers spring to life from a bulb that looks like a tomb. They remind us that believers will have a pure new life after they die because Jesus came back to life after He was crucified.

What You Need

- half sheet of typing paper or white construction paper
- pencil
- scissors
- transparent tape
- green pipe cleaner
- vase

What You Do

1. Lay a sheet of paper over the pattern on this page. Trace the pattern onto the paper and cut it out.

2. Roll the paper into the shape of an ice-cream cone. When the bottom edge is folded over to where it meets the dotted line, tape it in place.

3. Curl each petal point back by tightly winding it around your pencil as shown. Then unwind it.

4. Twist one end of the pipe cleaner into a ball. Stick the straight end through the inside of the flower and poke it through the small hole at the bottom of the flower to make a stem. Circle a piece of tape around the bottom of the flower to hold it on the pipe cleaner stem.

5. Put your flower in a vase. Make more lilies. They make a great centerpiece for your Easter dinner table!

EASTER
LILY
PATTERN

WRAP EDGE AROUND TO TOUCH THIS LINE AND TAPE HERE.

The Road to Emmaus

Something great happened to these disciples as they were walking from Jerusalem to Emmaus. What happened was so great that they turned around and hurried back to Jerusalem to tell everyone! With a pencil, lightly trace their way to Emmaus. The correct path has the missing words from the story below in the correct order. When you've traced the path, you can write the words in the blanks and read the story.
Put the words from the correct path into the blanks.

START HERE

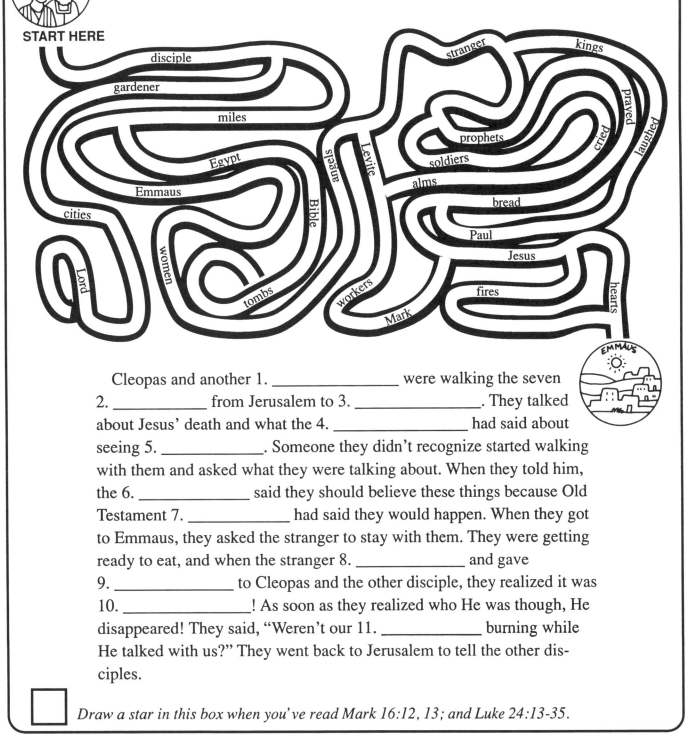

Cleopas and another 1. _____ were walking the seven 2. _____ from Jerusalem to 3. _____. They talked about Jesus' death and what the 4. _____ had said about seeing 5. _____. Someone they didn't recognize started walking with them and asked what they were talking about. When they told him, the 6. _____ said they should believe these things because Old Testament 7. _____ had said they would happen. When they got to Emmaus, they asked the stranger to stay with them. They were getting ready to eat, and when the stranger 8. _____ and gave 9. _____ to Cleopas and the other disciple, they realized it was 10. _____! As soon as they realized who He was though, He disappeared! They said, "Weren't our 11. _____ burning while He talked with us?" They went back to Jerusalem to tell the other disciples.

Draw a star in this box when you've read Mark 16:12, 13; and Luke 24:13-35.

19

Jesus Eats with the Disciples

Read about when Jesus appeared to the disciples and ate with them. Then find each underlined word from the story in the puzzle.

```
R  K  M  D  L  D  F  M  J  R  B
D  J  I  E  C  A  E  P  N  D  N
I  R  L  K  A  N  E  A  P  E  E
S  R  B  C  B  U  T  M  R  D  R
C  G  H  O  S  T  E  A  T  A  U
I  D  A  L  A  R  Z  O  P  A
P  O  N  R  B  I  S  E  D  N  L
L  B  D  F  I  S  H  D  B  T  H
E  W  S  R  K  U  B  I  J  O  E
S  N  Y  A  R  Y  M  A  V  B  I
```

The <u>disciples</u> were together in a room talking about Cleopas and his friend seeing Jesus on the road to Emmaus. The disciples had <u>locked</u> the door because they were afraid of the people who had killed Jesus. All of a sudden, even though the door was locked, Jesus was in the room! He said, "<u>Peace</u> be with you."

People don't often just pop into the middle of a room, so the disciples were afraid that they were seeing a <u>ghost</u> or something. Jesus said, "Why are you troubled, and why do doubts rise in your minds? Look at my hands and my <u>feet</u>. It is I myself! Touch me and see; a ghost does not have flesh and bones, as you see I have."

To reassure them, Jesus showed them His hands, feet, and side. Then the disciples were very happy but quite <u>amazed</u>. They found it hard to believe that this was really Jesus. He asked , "Do you have anything here to <u>eat</u>?" They gave Him a piece of cooked <u>fish</u>, and Jesus ate it.

Jesus said again, "Peace be with you! As the Father has sent me, I am sending you." Then He breathed on them and said, "Receive the Holy Spirit. If you forgive anyone his sins, they are forgiven; if you do not forgive them, they are not forgiven."

Draw a star in this box when you've read Mark 16:14; Luke 24:36-43; and John 20:19-23.

Doubting Thomas Believes

*Decode the underlined words in this story by changing each letter
to the one that comes before it in the alphabet. Then read the story.*

1. Uipnbt _____ wasn't with the other disciples when they
saw 2. Kftvt _____. When they told Thomas they had seen the
3. Mpse ____, he said, "Unless I see the 4. objm _____
marks in his hands and put my 5. gjohfs _____ where the nails
were, and put my 6. iboe ____ into His side, I will not believe
it."

One day when 7. Uipnbt _____ was with the disciples in a 8.
mpdlfe _____ room, Jesus suddenly was with them. He said,
9. "Qfbdf _____ be with you!"

Then Jesus looked at Thomas and said, "Put your 10. gjohfs
_____ here; see my hands. Reach out your hand and put it into
my side. Stop 11. epvcujoh _____ and believe."

Thomas said to Jesus, 12. "Nz __ Lord and my 13. Hpe ___!"

Jesus said, "Because you have seen me, you have 14.
cfmjfwfe _____; 15. cmfttfe _____ are those who have
not seen and yet have believed."

Jesus did many other16. njsbdmft _____ among His disciples. His appearances were 17. xsjuufo _____ so we would
believe that Jesus is the 18. Disjtu _____ (the one God sent),
the 19. Tpo ___ of God. If we believe in Jesus, we can have
eternal 20. mjgf ____.

Draw a star in this box when you've read John 20:24-31.

21

Seven Disciples Go Fishing

Find the fish in the code and then read this amazing story.

Peter, _____ , Nathanael, _____, John, and two other

_____ went fishing. They _____ all _____ but didn't

_____ a single fish! In the _____ the disciples saw a _____ they didn't

recognize standing on the _____. The man called out, "Friends, haven't you any

_____?" They said that they hadn't caught any.

The man said, "_____ your net on the right side of the _____ and you will

find some." The disciples did just what the man said, and they caught so many fish

they couldn't _____ in the net! They had to _____ it behind the _____!

John probably remembered when Jesus had done this three years earlier because he

22

THE FISH CODE

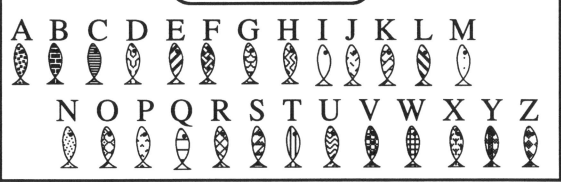

A B C D E F G H I J K L M

N O P Q R S T U V W X Y Z

told Peter, "It is the _____!" Peter was so excited to see Jesus that he put on his

[fish code]

cloak and _____ into the _____ to swim to shore! The other disciples

[fish code]   [fish code]

followed in the boat.

When the disciples reached the shore, they saw some _____ and a _____

[fish code]   [fish code]

with fish cooking on it. Jesus told them to bring some of the _____ they had just

[fish code]

caught and said, "Come and have _____." Jesus gave them bread and

[fish code]

fish and they all munched a good breakfast. The disciples didn't ask who He was.

They all knew He was _____. This was the _____ time Jesus appeared to

[fish code]   [fish code]

His disciples after His resurrection.

Draw a star in this box when you've read John 21:1-14.

Make a Fish Puppet

If you make a fish puppet, you can pretend he saw the disciples and Jesus. Have him tell the story from pages 22, 23 as if he were there.

What You Need

- sheet of colored construction paper
- scissors
- markers or crayons

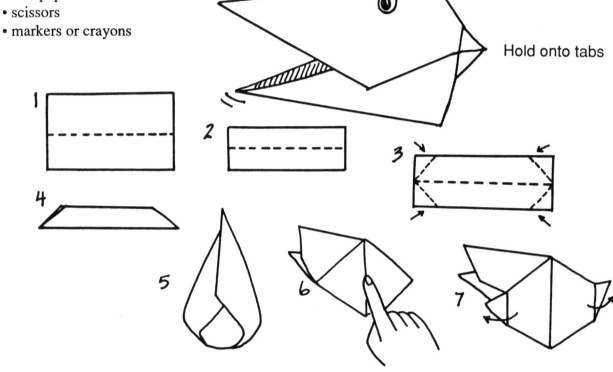

Hold onto tabs

What You Do

1. Fold the construction paper in half lengthwise and cut along the fold.
2. Fold one of the half sheets lengthwise; then unfold it.
3. Fold in each of the corners of the creased half sheet.
4. Fold the sheet in half lengthwise again with the bent corners inside.
5. Hold each end and bend the paper in half so that the ends overlap and the points meet. (You tuck one point inside of the other.)
6. This is the tricky step. Push in the back part of the fish's head. Crease the back so your fish is flat now.
7. Bend the tips of the back end of the fish outward. Hold onto these tips. As you pull on them, the fish will open and close its mouth.
8. Draw eyes on your fish with the crayons or markers. Now you can tell a true fish tale!

Make an 'Eat-able' Scene

Make this scene to remind you of Jesus filling the disciples' nets with fish.

What You Need

- 1/2 of a boiled egg
- 1/2 slice of cheese, cut as a triangle
- toothpick
- cooked spaghetti noodles (with a few drops of oil stirred into them)
- fish crackers

What You Do

1. Stick the toothpick through the cheese slice and poke it into the boiled egg to make the boat.
2. Weave the spaghetti noodles to look like a net.
3. Put the fish crackers inside the net.

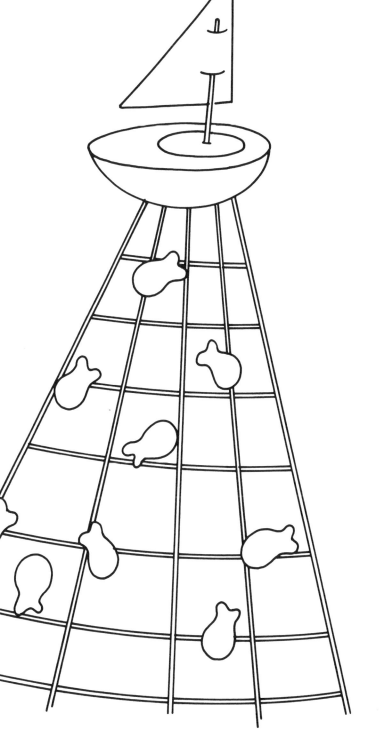

Do You Love Me?

When Jesus and His disciples finished eating some of the fish they caught, Jesus and Simon Peter had a conversation that was almost the same three times. *Read their conversation and then color the pictures.*

Feed His Sheep

Jesus told Peter that if he loved Him, Peter should take care of Jesus' sheep. Jesus' sheep are His followers. Peter was told to take care of Jesus' followers, both young and old. If we love Jesus, we'll help Jesus' followers, too. Feeding them can mean giving them food for their bodies or giving them food for their spirits.

On each lamb, write the name of someone you know who follows Jesus. In each bowl, write a way you can help that lamb.

☐ *Draw a star in this box when you've read John 21:15-24.*

One BIG Book!

Jesus did even more things than are written about in the Bible. Jesus' disciple John said that if everything Jesus did were written down, he didn't think the whole world would have room for all that would be written! Now that would be one big book!

Make a Book

Write and illustrate your own book about what Jesus has done for you.

What You Need

- 5 sheets of plain paper
- one sheet of construction paper
- scissors
- ribbon
- markers or crayons

What You Do

1. Lay the sheets of plain paper on top of the sheet of construction paper. Fold them in half and then open them up.

2. With the scissors, make two small holes on the fold, with each hole about one third of the way in from the edge of the book. String the ribbon through the holes and tie it tightly so it holds your book together.

3. On the cover, write "What Jesus Has Done for Me" and draw a picture of yourself with Jesus.

4. On each page inside the book, draw a picture of something Jesus has done for you and write a sentence about it at the bottom of the page.

Draw a star in this box when you've read John 21:25.

On a Mountain in Galilee

The eleven disciples went to a mountain in Galilee. Jesus had told them to go there, and when they saw Jesus, they worshiped Him. This may be when more than five hundred others also saw Jesus. *Find each shape in the code and write its letter to spell out what Jesus told His disciples.*

CODE

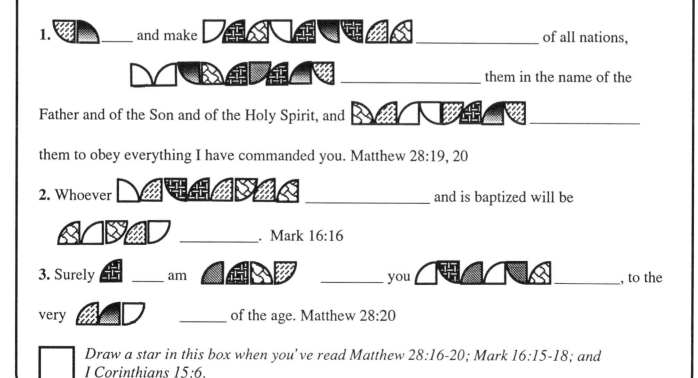

1. _____ and make _____ of all nations, _____ them in the name of the Father and of the Son and of the Holy Spirit, and _____ them to obey everything I have commanded you. Matthew 28:19, 20

2. Whoever _____ and is baptized will be _____. Mark 16:16

3. Surely ____ am _____ you _____, to the very _____ of the age. Matthew 28:20

Draw a star in this box when you've read Matthew 28:16-20; Mark 16:15-18; and I Corinthians 15:6.

29

I Am with You Always

What do you picture when you think of yourself praying? Do you see yourself kneeling by your bed at night or bowing your head before eating a meal? Those are good times to pray, but they aren't the only times we can pray.

Jesus said to His disciples, "Surely I am with you always." He is with you always, too, wherever you are and whatever you are doing. You can pray *anytime* and God will hear you and help you.

Look at each of the situations below. Have you ever found yourself in a similar situation? Think of something you could silently pray if that were happening to you, and write your prayer in the little cloud.

HEY, SIS, YOU'RE PRETTY BRAVE TO BE MY FIRST PASSENGER SINCE I GOT MY LICENSE.

I FEEL LOUSY.

Draw a star in this box when you've read Matthew 28:20.

30

The Great Commission

Jesus wants us to tell people everywhere the good news that they will go to heaven if they will trust Him as Savior. Find each continent on the map. Then find the name of each continent in one of the words in the story below that has all capital letters. When you find the continent's name, cross out the letters of the name. When you have crossed out all the continents, you will find what Jesus said to His disciples in Mark 16:15.

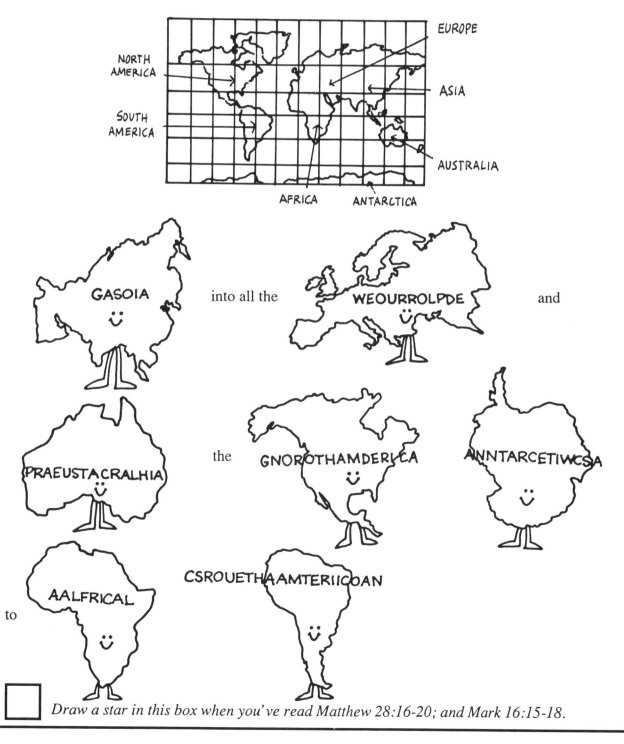

GASOIA   into all the   WEOURROLPDE   and

the   GNOROTHAMDERLCA   ANNTARCETIWCSA

PRAEUSTACRALHIA

to   AALFRICAL   CSROUETHAAMTERIICOAN

Draw a star in this box when you've read Matthew 28:16-20; and Mark 16:15-18.

31

The Kingdom of Heaven

When people decide to obey Jesus as their King, they become part of His kingdom. Jesus loves us and wants us to be in His kingdom. He wants us to help other people come into it, too.

Pick the Pictures

Match the pictures with the parables that Jesus told about the kingdom of heaven.

1. The Kingdom of heaven is like yeast. It makes bread dough light and airy instead of hard and flat so that it tastes better. When people let Jesus rule them, He changes them for the better.

2. The message about the Kingdom is like seeds a farmer plants. If he plants them in good soil, they will grow. God wants us to let His message grow in our hearts so good things will come out of us.

3. The Kingdom is like treasure hidden in a field. When a man found it, he hid it again. Then he sold everything he had and bought the field. When people discover the great rewards of following Jesus, they will give up whatever God asks in order to follow Him.

4. The Kingdom is like a merchant. When he found a beautiful pearl that was worth a lot of money, he sold everything he had and bought it. When someone finds out that following Jesus is worth more than everything else, he is willing to give up ways of life that weren't as good.

5. The Kingdom is like a net that caught all kinds of fish. The fishermen pulled the net onto the shore and collected the good fish in baskets but threw the bad ones away. Someday angels will separate evil people from those who are right with God.

6. The Kingdom is like a tiny mustard seed planted in a field. Mustard seeds grow into large trees. Jesus' kingdom started very small, but He has millions of followers now. His kingdom is still growing!

7. The Kingdom is like a man scattering seeds on the ground. The seeds sprout, grow, and become grain. When the grain is ripe, the man harvests the grain. God's kingdom is growing. When He is ready, God will gather up the people who are part of His kingdom.

8. The Kingdom is like a man whose enemy planted weeds in his wheat field. When the wheat grew, so did the weeds. At harvest time, the owner's helpers got rid of the weeds and brought the wheat into the barn. One day Jesus will weed out of His kingdom everything that causes sin and all who do evil.

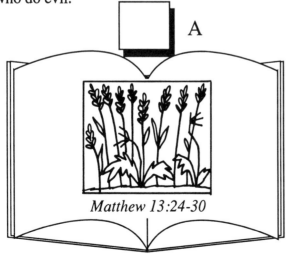

A

Matthew 13:24-30

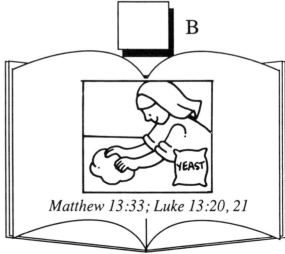

B

Matthew 13:33; Luke 13:20, 21

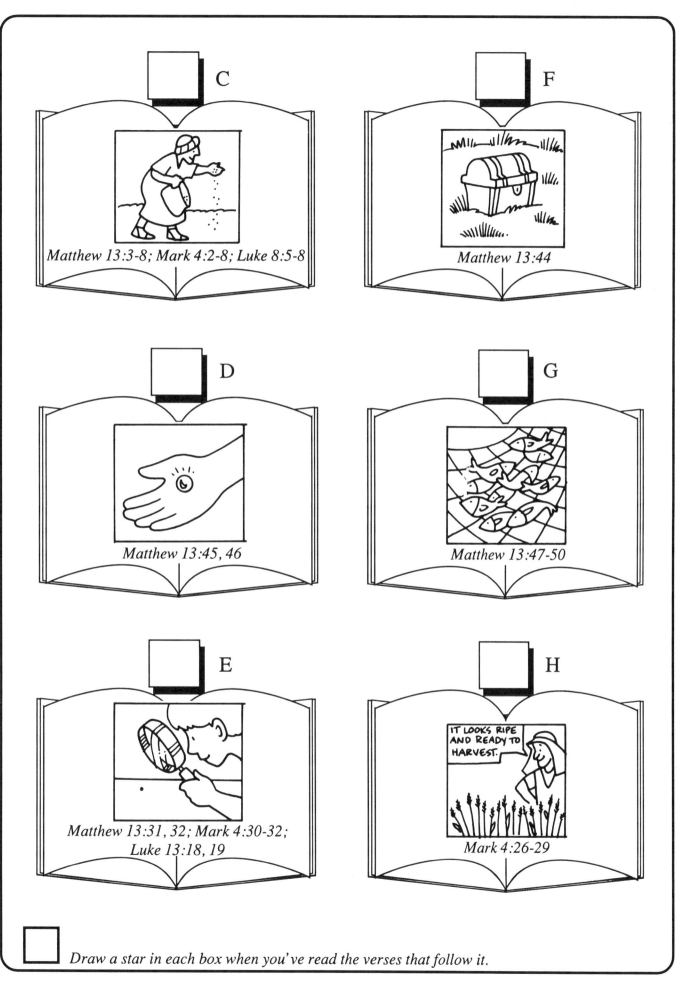

C

Matthew 13:3-8; Mark 4:2-8; Luke 8:5-8

F

Matthew 13:44

D

Matthew 13:45, 46

G

Matthew 13:47-50

E

Matthew 13:31, 32; Mark 4:30-32;
Luke 13:18, 19

H

IT LOOKS RIPE
AND READY TO
HARVEST.

Mark 4:26-29

Draw a star in each box when you've read the verses that follow it.

Wait for the Gift

After His resurrection, Jesus appeared to the disciples during a period of forty days. He spoke about the kingdom of God. One time while He was eating with them, He commanded them not to leave Jerusalem but to wait for the gift His Father had promised. He said the gift would give them power. Do you know what the gift was? *On the gift below, color in all the shapes with a dot to find the answer.*

Draw a star in this box when you've read Luke 24:44-49; and Acts 1:3-8.

Jesus Goes Up to Heaven

Jesus led His disciples to a place near Bethany and lifted up His hands and blessed them. But the next thing the disciples knew, they were watching Jesus being taken up into heaven! Soon a cloud hid Jesus from their sight and He was gone!

The disciples were looking up into the sky trying to see Jesus when suddenly two men wearing white stood beside them.

To decode what the heavenly messengers said to the disciples about Jesus, write the letter that begins each picture in the blank beneath it.

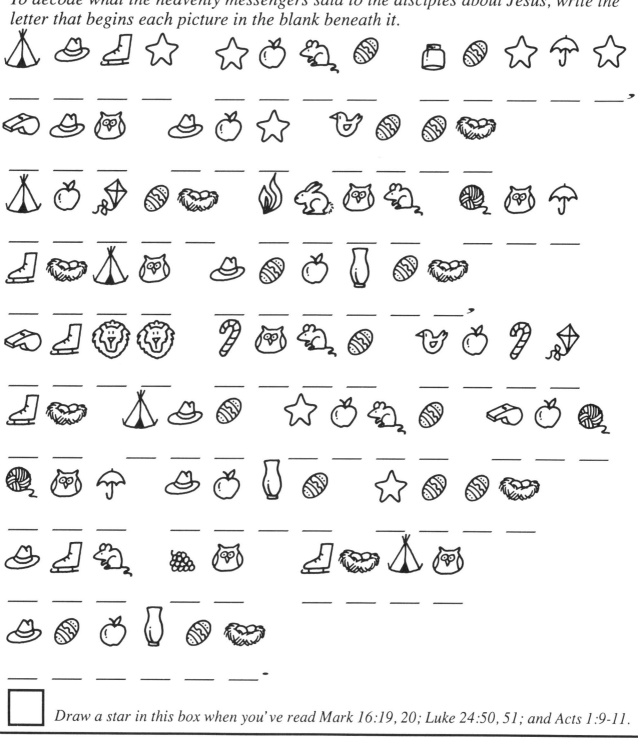

Draw a star in this box when you've read Mark 16:19, 20; Luke 24:50, 51; and Acts 1:9-11.

He's Coming Again!

Do you like surprises? The greatest surprise of all will be when Jesus returns to earth. That's called the Second Coming. No one except God the Father knows exactly when the Second Coming will be. However, many of the things that will happen before Jesus returns are listed in Matthew 24 and Mark 13.

The important thing is to be ready for Jesus' return. *Decode one of the things that Jesus said would happen before He came back which will help people be ready for His return. Find each number on the calendar and write the letter from that date.*

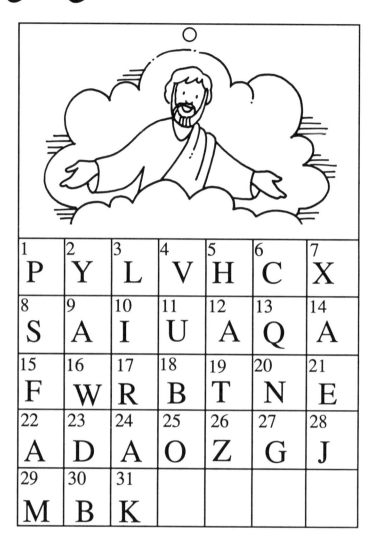

1	2	3	4	5	6	7
P	Y	L	V	H	C	X
8	9	10	11	12	13	14
S	A	I	U	A	Q	A
15	16	17	18	19	20	21
F	W	R	B	T	N	E
22	23	24	25	26	27	28
A	D	A	O	Z	G	J
29	30	31				
M	B	K				

‾19‾ ‾5‾ ‾10‾ ‾8‾ ‾27‾ ‾25‾ ‾8‾ ‾1‾ ‾21‾ ‾3‾ ‾25‾ ‾15‾ ‾19‾ ‾5‾ ‾21‾

‾31‾ ‾10‾ ‾20‾ ‾27‾ ‾23‾ ‾25‾ ‾29‾ ‾16‾ ‾10‾ ‾3‾ ‾3‾ ‾18‾ ‾21‾

‾1‾ ‾17‾ ‾21‾ ‾9‾ ‾6‾ ‾5‾ ‾21‾ ‾23‾ ‾10‾ ‾20‾ ‾19‾ ‾5‾ ‾21‾

‾16‾ ‾5‾ ‾25‾ ‾3‾ ‾21‾ ‾16‾ ‾25‾ ‾17‾ ‾3‾ ‾23‾. Matthew 24:14.

Draw a star in this box when you've read Matthew 16:2, 3; 24:14, 32, 33, 36; Mark 13:28, 29, 32; Luke 12:56; 21:29-31.

Jesus Will Surprise Many

Jesus said that many people won't be expecting Him when He returns. He wants people to get ready for His coming by accepting Him as Savior and following Him as Lord. When He comes, He wants to find us serving Him.

To find out what Jesus said His coming would be like, connect the dots below to make the picture.

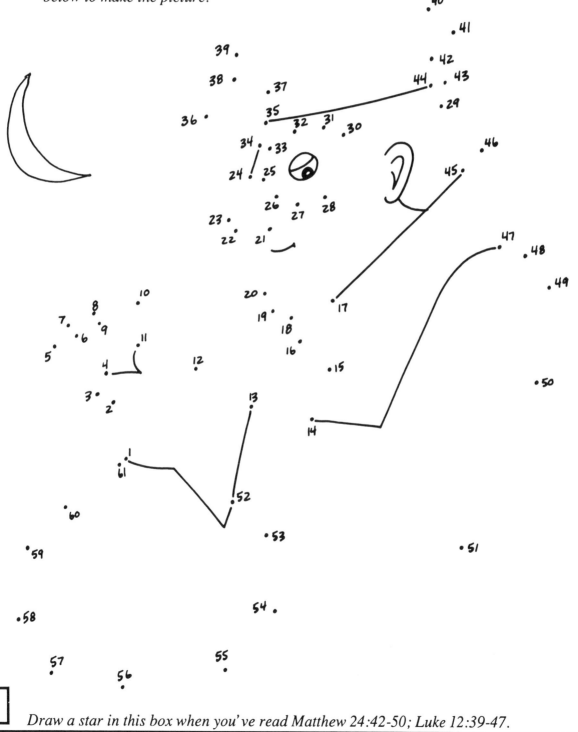

Draw a star in this box when you've read Matthew 24:42-50; Luke 12:39-47.

Like in the Days of Noah

Jesus said His return will catch a lot of people by surprise, just like the Flood in Noah's day surprised a lot of people. Noah got ready for the Flood by taking his family and animals into the ark to keep them safe. We need to be ready for the Second Coming by entering the "ark of salvation." If you want to be ready when Jesus returns and get on the ark of salvation right now by trusting Him as the only way to heaven, pray a prayer like this in your own words:

Dear God,
Thank You for sending Your Son, Jesus, to take the punishment for my sins. I am sorry for the wrong things I have done. Please take away my sins. Please come into my life and give me eternal life.
In Jesus' name. Amen.

Enter the Ark

After you have fun making this ark and animals, you can write your name and the names of your family members and friends on the people. If any of them aren't Christians yet, tell them how they can "get on the ark" by praying to accept Jesus as their Savior.

What You Need

- typing or construction paper
- scissors
- ink pad
- watercolor markers
- stapler

How to Make the Animals

1. Cut small paper rectangles and fold them in half so they stand.
2. Press your fingertip onto an ink pad and make fingerprints on both sides of the stand-up rectangles.
3. Draw legs and other features on the fingerprints to make them look like animals. You can also make fingerprint people for Noah and the seven other members of his family.

How to Make the Ark

1. Fold a full sheet of paper in half and staple two sides together, but leave the top open (like an envelope).
2. Draw an ark on both sides of the envelope.
3. You can store the animals in the ark.
When you see your ark, remember that accepting Jesus as your Savior will save you, just like the ark saved the animals and Noah from the Flood.

Draw a star in this box when you've read Matthew 24:37-39; and Luke 17:26, 27.

Sheep and Goats

Jesus said one day He will divide people into groups the way a shepherd separates sheep from goats. Jesus said that only the people who are like the sheep will stay with Him. *Read Matthew 25:35, 36, and write in the blanks below what the sheep did for Jesus. When we do things for people, it is like we're doing them for Jesus. Can you think of ways you can help people?*

1. I was _____ and you gave Me something to _____.

2. I was _____ and you gave Me something to _____.

3. I didn't know anyone and you _____ Me in.

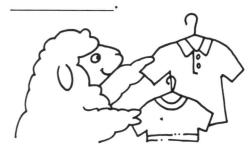

4. I needed _____ and you gave Me things to wear.

5. I was _____ and you looked after Me.

6. I was in _____ and you came to _____ Me.

☐ *Draw a star in this box when you've read Matthew 25:31-46.*

The Second Coming

Circle the right answers about Jesus' return.

1. Jesus will come on
_____ in the sky
with power and glory.

a fiery chariot   clouds   an airplane

2. A _____ will
sound.

harp   smoke detector   trumpet

3. He'll send _____
to gather His followers
from around the world.

cars   angels   invitations

4. _____ will see
Him.

Only children   Only believers   Everyone

Draw a star in this box when you've read Matthew 24:30, 31; Mark 13:26, 27; Luke 21:27; and Revelation 1:7.

Jesus' Return

When Jesus returns, people who have asked Him to be their Savior will be caught up in the clouds to meet Him in the air. This is called "the Rapture." It will happen very quickly when people are doing everyday things. No one knows when this will happen, but if it were to happen tomorrow, what do you think you might be doing?

Make a Balloon Self-Portrait

People who are filled with faith in Jesus are like balloons filled with helium. Believers will rise up into the air to meet Jesus when He comes! Make a balloon self-portrait to remind you to be filled with faith that Jesus took the punishment for your sins so you can go to heaven. If you haven't asked Him to be your Savior yet, you can do it right now.

What You Need
- air-filled balloon
- permanent markers
- pencil
- cardboard
- scissors

What You Do
1. Draw your head and body on the balloon with permanent markers.
2. On a piece of cardboard, trace around your feet or shoes with the pencil. Make sure your feet are close together; don't trace each one separately.
3. Draw your toenails or shoestrings on the cardboard feet or shoes.
4. Cut out your footprints. Make a small slit in the middle, and poke the knot of the balloon through it.

☐ *Draw a star in this box when you've read Luke 17:30-37 and I Thessalonians 4:17.*

Heaven

If we trust Jesus to save us and we show our faith by following Him, we will live with Him someday in heaven! He has gone to prepare a place for us! Can you imagine what it will be like? We will all be very happy there!

What Will Heaven Be Like?

Draw an X over the things that won't be in heaven.

Draw a star in this box when you've read John 14:2-6; Revelation 14:2, 3; 21:4, 23; and 22:5.

ANSWERS

Page 6   1. Lord 2. Peter 3. body 4. angels 5. crying 6. Jesus 7. gardener 8. Father

Page 19   1. disciple 2. miles 3. Emmaus 4. women 5. angels 6. stranger 7. prophets 8. prayed
          9. bread 10. Jesus 11. hearts

Page 20

```
R K M D L D F M J R B
D J I E C A E P N D N
I R L K A N E A P E E
S R B C B U T M R D R
C G H O S T E A T A U
I D A L A X R Z O P A
P O N R B I S E D N L
L B D F I S H D B T H
E W S R K U B I J O E
S N Y A R Y M A V B I
```

Page 21   1. Thomas 2. Jesus 3. Lord 4. nail 5. finger 6. hand 7. Thomas 8. locked 9. Peace
          10. finger 11. doubting 12. My 13. God 14. believed 15. blessed 16. miracles
          17. written 18. Christ 19. Son 20. life

Page 22-23   Peter, Thomas, Nathanael, James, John, and two other disciples went fishing. They
          fished all night but didn't catch a single fish! In the morning the disciples saw a man they
          didn't recognize standing on the shore. The man called out, "Friends, haven't you any
          fish?" They said that they hadn't caught any.
               The man said, "Throw your net on the right side of the boat and you will find some."
          The disciples did just what the man said, and they caught so many fish they couldn't haul
          in the net! They had to drag it behind the boat! John probably remembered when Jesus
          had done this three years earlier because he told Peter, "It is the Lord!" Peter was so
          excited to see Jesus that he put on his cloak and jumped into the water to swim to shore!
          The other disciples followed in the boat.
               When the disciples reached the shore, they saw some bread and a fire with fish cook-
          ing on it. Jesus told them to bring some of the fish they had just caught and said, "Come
          and have breakfast." Jesus gave them bread and fish and they all munched a good break-
          fast. The disciples didn't ask who He was. They all knew He was Jesus. This was the
          third time Jesus appeared to His disciples after His resurrection.

Page 29   1. Go and make disciples of all nations, baptizing them in the name of the Father and of
          the Son and of the Holy Spirit, and teaching them to obey everything I have commanded
          you. Matthew 28: 19, 20
          2. Whoever believes and is baptized will be saved. Mark 16:16
          3. Surely I am with you always, to the very end of the age. Matthew 28: 20

ANSWERS

Page 31   Go, world, preach, good, news, all, creation

Pages 32-33 1. B   2. C   3. F   4. D   5. G   6. E   7. H   8. A

Page 34   The Holy Spirit

Page 35   This same Jesus, who has been taken from you into heaven, will come back in the same way you have seen Him go into heaven.

Page 36   This gospel of the kingdom will be preached in the whole world.

Page 37

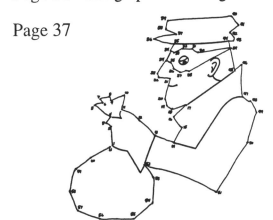

Page 39   1. hungry, eat 2. thirsty, drink 3. invited 4. clothes 5. sick 6. prison, visit

Page 40   1. clouds 2. trumpet 3. angels 4. Everyone

Page 42   Nighttime, tears, death, and sickness should be crossed out.

I DID IT!

COMPLETED	DATE	COMPLETED	DATE
☐ The First Easter, Part 1	_____	☐ Make a Fish Puppet	_____
☐ The First Easter, Part 2	_____	☐ Make an 'Eat-able' Scene	_____
☐ Make Glove Puppets	_____	☐ Do You Love Me?	_____
☐ Make an Egg Scene	_____	☐ One BIG Book!	_____
☐ Easter Story Hunt	_____	☐ On a Mountain in Galilee	_____
☐ Christian Meanings of Easter Symbols	_____	☐ I Am with You Always	_____
☐ Make Easter Stickers	_____	☐ The Great Commission	_____
☐ Easter Eggs	_____	☐ The Kingdom of Heaven (Kingdom Parables)	_____
☐ Easter Chicks	_____	☐ Wait for the Gift	_____
☐ Eggshell Mosaic Cross	_____	☐ Jesus Goes up to Heaven	_____
☐ Jonah and the Great Fish	_____	☐ He Is Coming Again!	_____
☐ Make a Lamb Cupcake	_____	☐ Jesus Will Surprise Many	_____
☐ Make Paper Easter Lilies	_____	☐ Like in the Days of Noah	_____
☐ The Road to Emmaus	_____	☐ Sheep and Goats	_____
☐ Jesus Eats with the Disciples	_____	☐ The Second Coming	_____
☐ Doubting Thomas Believes	_____	☐ Jesus' Return	_____
☐ Seven Disciples Go Fishing	_____	☐ Heaven	_____

Index of *The Life and Lessons of Jesus* Series

Index of *The Life and Lessons of Jesus* Series

*If you would like to write the author,
send your letter to:*

Your address here

Put
stamp
here

Tracy L. Harrast
c/o Church Resources Dept.
David C. Cook Publishing Co.
850 N. Grove Avenue
Elgin, IL 60120